Fishing on the Football Field

Story By Anthony and Devon Policci

For sons, daughters, parents, and the joy of sharing life's simple moments and grand adventures.
To children of all ages and the child inside each adult who still longs for adventure.

Published by Absolutely Brilliant Concepts, Inc. and Adventures With Dad™ Publications
©2021 ABC M&C Inc.
Text copyright ©2010 Anthony and Devon Policci
Illustration copyright © 2020 Anthony Policci

Visit our website at www.policcifamily.com

First Edition
Printed in the USA

Library of Congress Control Number: 2021910745

Summary: Devon and his friends discover their school's football/soccer field is flooded.
There are a dozen or so fish swimming in the water. How did this happen, and what can be done?

ISBN: 978-1-7372379-0-7

MY NAME IS DEVON POLICCI

This story is true.

I was ten years old and living in the United States of America in Chandler, Arizona, when this happened to me.

I hope you enjoy it.

It was almost noon on a Saturday in December. I was still in bed because I stayed up too late the night before playing video games.

I had been awake for a while, but I didn't want to get out of bed because I had nothing planned for the day.

I don't know about you, but I feel sad when I have not planned something to do over the weekend.

After all, my time is short. I only have two days free from school, so I want to pack as much fun as possible into those two days!

But this Saturday, I had no idea what I was going to do with the day, so I wasn't very excited about getting up.

I didn't know it at the time, but the day had plans for me.

I was in for an adventure.

The feeling in my tummy forced me to get out of bed, and I made my way downstairs to eat a bowl of cereal.

All I could think about was when the next break from school would be.

The November holiday had come and gone, and it seemed like it would be forever before the holidays in December.

As the last few bites of my cereal disappeared, I started thinking of what I would do next.

It was already past lunchtime, and here I was, only finishing breakfast. In my mind, the day was already half over, and I didn't know what to do with myself.

I put my bowl in the sink and decided I would find one of my family members to give me some ideas.

First, I went to find my dad. My dad is pretty awesome. He looks a lot like the superhero Tony Stark; you know, "Iron Man," and his name is Tony in real life too. I hoped he would have some good ideas for something to do.

Well, my dad was busy cleaning the garage. He said he would be busy for a while longer, but I could help him clean if I were bored.

Dad always suggests that I do chores when I'm bored. Yuck! I didn't want to do that!

Didn't he realize my Saturday was slipping away from me?

I needed to do something fun, or it would feel like I wasted one of my two weekend days!

My mom was sick and in bed. She had been ill for a few days, so I knew there was no chance of getting any ideas from her.

So I went to see what my brother Michael was doing.

I found him playing video games.

He was so focused on getting to the next mission in the game there was no chance of getting him to do something with me.

I was feeling impatient.

I had wasted at least two minutes so far, and I wasn't going to sit there and wait for my brother to get tired of his game.

I knew then that I had to take emergency boredom prevention measures.

It was time to see if my friend Andres could play.

Andres lived three houses down the street, so I had to run upstairs and change out of my pajamas.

I ran back downstairs and out the door, hollering to my dad as I went, "Dad, I'm going to Andres' house!"

One minute later, I was ringing his doorbell and banging on the door as if my life depended on it.

Andres answered the door, all excited because he had just gotten back from the store with his very first pet - a HAMSTER!

He had named this hamster Jesus. That's pronounced, "Hey-Zeus."

He was brown and white, and very playful.

We played with that little hamster for about an hour. We let him run all over the house in his exercise ball, but after a while, we had gotten a bit tired of it.
And then we heard the doorbell ring.

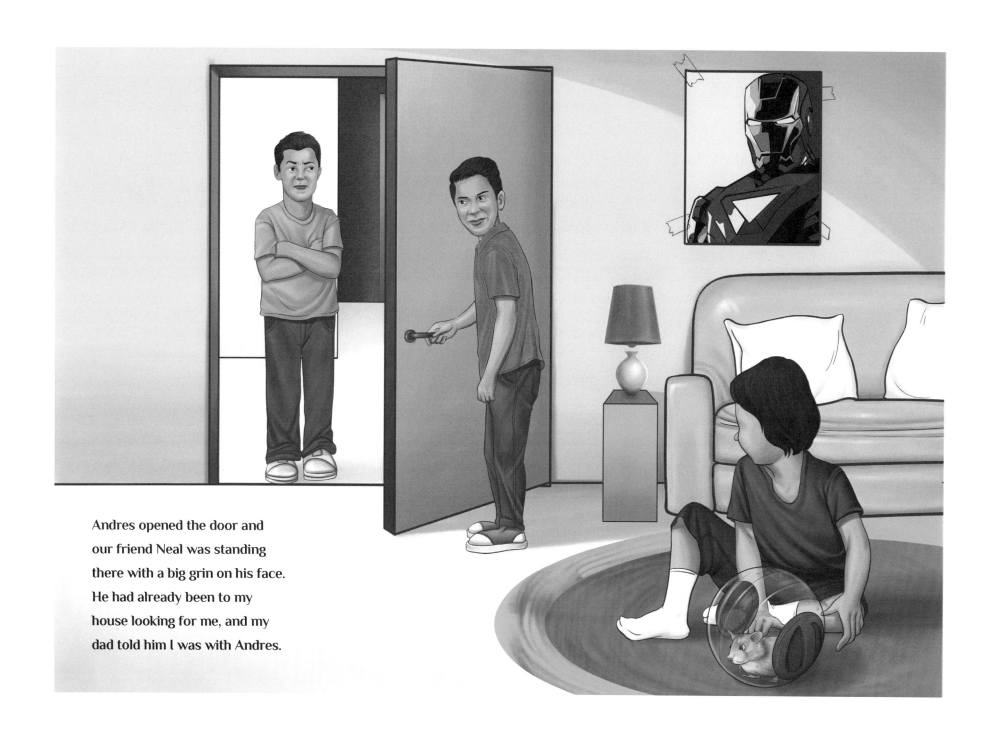

Andres opened the door and
our friend Neal was standing
there with a big grin on his face.
He had already been to my
house looking for me, and my
dad told him I was with Andres.

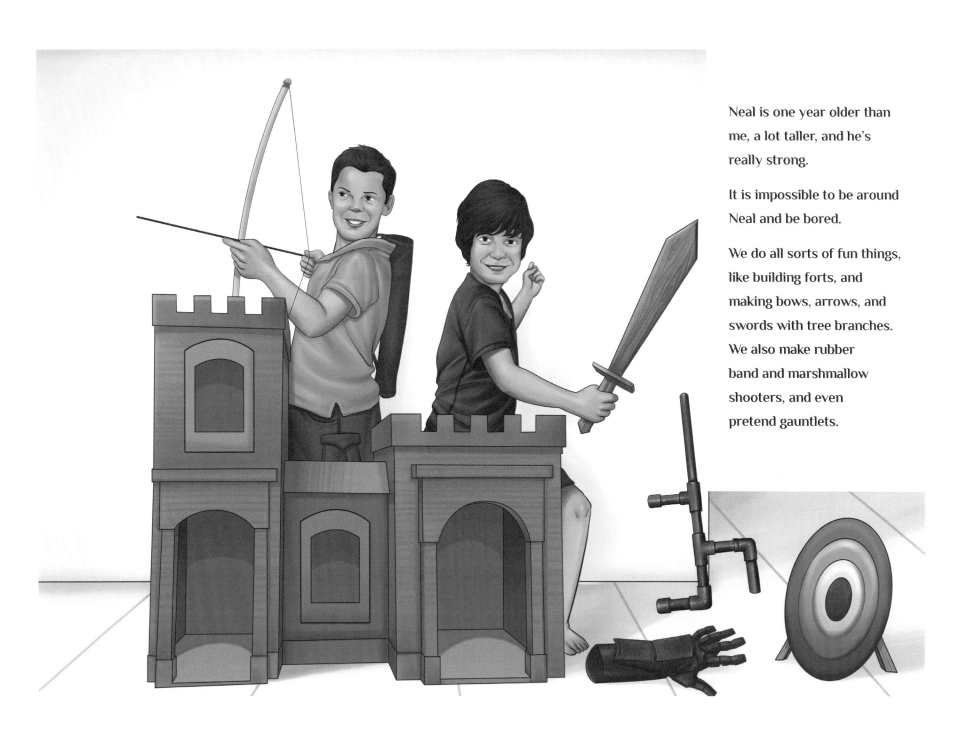

Neal is one year older than me, a lot taller, and he's really strong.

It is impossible to be around Neal and be bored.

We do all sorts of fun things, like building forts, and making bows, arrows, and swords with tree branches. We also make rubber band and marshmallow shooters, and even pretend gauntlets.

Neal said that since it was a cloudy day, we should light off some fireworks. Fireworks are only allowed in certain cities and only on certain days in Arizona.

We didn't live in one of those cities, and it wasn't one of those days.

So the thought of doing something we weren't allowed to do, which could get us into real trouble, sounded like a fantastic idea.

There was only one problem...we had no fireworks!

Then I remembered our trip down to Mexico before the 4th of July. We had bought a bunch of fireworks to light on the beach.

We had somehow forgotten to use one of the boxes of fireworks and only discovered it after we got back to Arizona. My dad hid them somewhere and told us we would use them the next year.

Now we had a mission - find them!

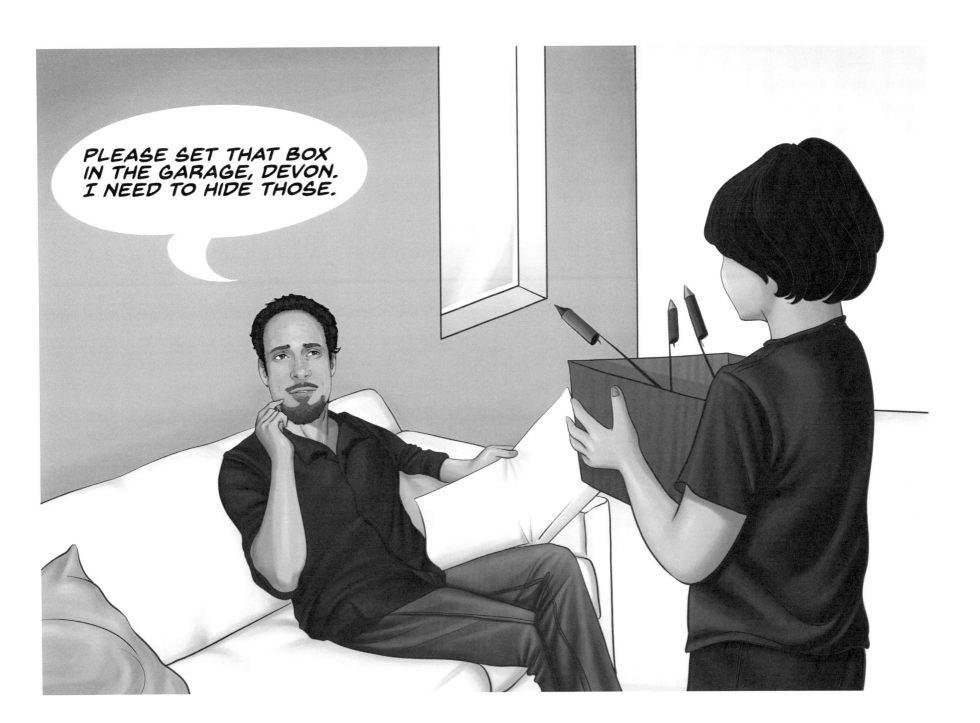

We first started searching for them in my garage. My dad had gone back in the house to do some laundry, and we pretty much tore through every inch of that garage and came up empty.

We were upset that we couldn't find the fireworks. Then we thought, "maybe they are up in the attic.

In Arizona, most of the houses don't have real attics; this was more like a storage area up in the ceiling in the garage. The cool thing about it was my dad had nailed big flat pieces of wood all over the inside of the ceiling so we could walk wherever we wanted up there without falling through.

We got the ladder out and climbed up. No luck there either.

On the way out of the attic, I slipped and almost fell, but Neal being the strong guy he is, reached out and caught me before I dropped.

That was when we decided to do something a little safer and go to the park with our homemade bow and arrows.

There were a lot of grown-ups with little kids at the park, so we decided to walk over to our school.

The school is right next to the park and has a playground.

There are also fields for baseball, football, and soccer.

When we got there, we noticed something incredible.

The football field looked like a lake – it was flooded!

We were very excited after seeing this. Although it was December, the temperature in Arizona is much warmer than in other states.

We decided we would run around in the water and pretend we were hunting in a giant swamp.

As we were walking around shooting our homemade arrows, we suddenly noticed something moving in the water.

What could be?

It was quick and darted through the water. No, it couldn't be.

Then we saw it again, and then we noticed movement in four or five different places on the field. We almost couldn't believe our eyes!

The water on the football field was filled with...

FISH!

There were at least two dozen fish. Big fish, medium fish, little fish. Fish swimming out on our football and soccer field. It was crazy!

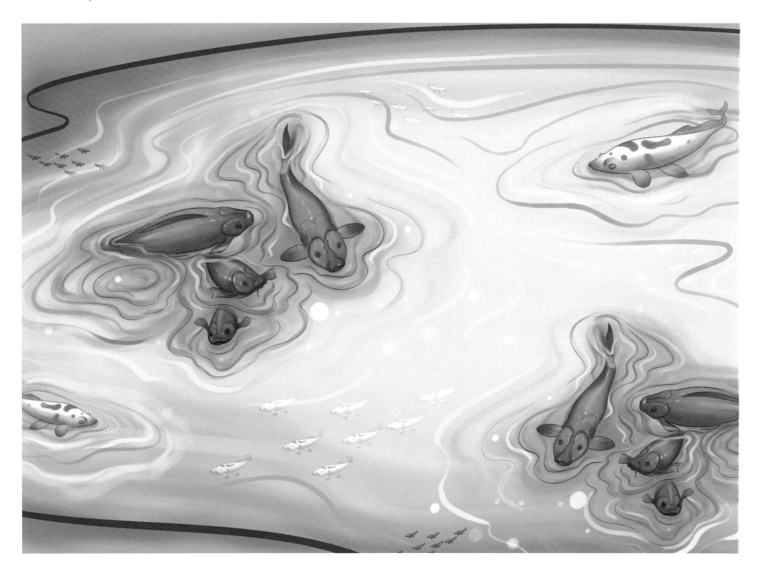

We had no idea how this could have happened, but we were so excited we ran back to my house to get something to catch them.

When we got back, my dad was in the garage again. The first thing out of his mouth was, "why is the ladder out."

We didn't tell him we were looking for fireworks. Instead, all three of us blurted out different versions of "*the school football field is flooded…and there are f-f-f-fish everywhere!*"

My dad gave us a funny look and just said, "let me walk over there with you so you guys can show me what you're trying to tell me."

As we got over to the school grounds and started walking around the fields, my dad saw the fish and said we need to go back and get our rain boots and a bucket to see if we could rescue them.

We asked, "what do you mean rescue?" and dad then started pointing out that the water had been slowly draining off the field, and now it was getting so low in some spots that the fish were winding up getting stuck in areas where there was not enough water to swim.

We needed those buckets, and we needed them fast!

But while we were getting buckets at our house, Andre's brother came over and told him it was time to go home.

Then Neil decided to leave too.

So, dad and I went back to school alone

There we were, just us two with our buckets, trying to rescue the fish.

This was not easy. Have you ever tried to catch a fish with your bare hands?

Even in the shallow water, they were way too fast for us. So we figured out a plan and worked together as a team.

We would stand away from each other and walk in the same direction to scare the fish away from us. This caused them to swim to areas on the field where the water was very shallow.

They would end up in the grass, and we would pick them up and put them in a bucket with the water in it. We kept at it and caught every live fish that we could find.

Pretty soon, it was too dark to see anymore, and we were soaking wet and cold. So, we grabbed our buckets and made our way home.

We put the fish in bigger buckets in our garage and went inside to clean up and put on dry clothes.

Then we made something for dinner and told my mom about the fish and showed them to my brother.

We talked about what we were going to do with the fish we'd saved.

My dad thought the best thing to do was find one of the local community lakes that already had fish in it and release them into that.

That night as I got ready for bed, I felt terrific about the fish we could help. But I was worried if they would be okay in those buckets all night.

The next morning, I was up bright and early, and so was my dad. He said he figured out a place to take the fish and release them before we got ready for church. We tried to wake my brother up to see if he wanted to come with us. But he was sleeping like a rock.

Dad and I went out and checked on the fish. They were all still alive, which was terrific. We picked up the buckets, got into our car, and drove the fish to a nearby community lake.

We carried the fish in the buckets to the edge of the water and released them one by one.

Each one of them swam away quickly and seemed very happy. All in all, we had a few dozen small and medium-sized fish and one massive one.

After we released all the fish, we climbed back into our car. Both of us had big smiles on our faces. We didn't say anything to each other, but I knew my dad felt the same thing I did.

It was a real adventure, and we'd saved those fish's lives.

My weekend started out looking like it would be a boring waste of time but turned out to be one of the most memorable and exciting days ever.

My dad later explained that the fish somehow got transferred into the canal water that was pumped onto the field to water the grass. I've seen the football
fields flooded many more times since that day in December, and I always went
back over to look for fish.

So far, there hasn't been any more.

I guess this was a once-in-a-lifetime experience. I don't know about Andres
or Neal, but my dad and I will never forget the day we went fishing
on the football field.

ABOUT THE AUTHOR

At the time of this story, Devon Policci, his brother Michael and their friends Neal
and Andres were all students at Santan Elementary School in Chandler, Arizona.
It happened on December 4, 2010.

Devon was a very active ten-year-old. He played the violin and keyboard, had won multiple
first-place awards in karate tournaments, wrestled, rode a pro-scooter, sang in the chorus
at his school, did parkour, was an avid trampoline enthusiast, and could do endless backflips.

Devon loved airsoft and paintball, was routinely on the honor roll, and even had the lead in
his school's first-ever full-length stage production of "Your Good Man Charlie Brown.

Devon's dad has been nicknamed "Tony Stark" for years, and he helped Devon with portions
of this story.

The entire story is 100% true

Lightning Source UK Ltd.
Milton Keynes UK
UKRC041155170822
407434UK00001B/5